D1623118

Effective Multiplication Strategies
for the Local Church

STAN TOLER

STANTOLER
developing leaders

Stan Toler is a dynamic international speaker, having spoken in over 80 countries of the world. He has written over 100 books, including his best-sellers, *The Secret Blend; Richest Person in the World; Five Secrets of An Exceptional Leader, The Inspirational Speaker's Resource, ReThink Your Life*, his popular *Minute Motivator for Leaders* series, *Total Quality Life, TERRIFIC! Five Star Customer Service* and his newest book, *Outstanding! Leadership that Motivates and Relates.* His books have sold over 3 million copies. Toler for many years served as Vice-President and taught seminars for John C. Maxwell's INJOY Leadership Institute training church and corporate leaders to make a difference in the world.

www.StanToler.com – Stan@StanToler.com

WHAT IS EVANGELISM?

Then Jesus came to them and said, "All authority in heaven and on earth has been given to me. Therefore go and make disciples of all nations, baptizing them in the name of the Father and of the Son and of the Holy Spirit, and teaching them to obey everything I have commanded you. And surely I am with you always, to the very end of the age" (Matthew 28:18-20).

1. Evangelism is a process of _____.

2. Evangelism produces _____ life.

3. Evangelism meets _____.

4. Evangelism is sharing the _____.

5. Evangelism is only _____ when a person enters a relationship with Christ.

WITNESS (wit'nes) *n.* 1. a. One who has seen or heard something. b. One who gives evidence. 2. To serve as or furnish evidence of.

Obstacles to Vision and Outreach

What is vision? It is simply making the invisible visible—a clear mental image of a future imparted by God to us, His servants.

1. Indecisive _____.

2. Ingrown _____.

3. Inadequate _____.

4. Insufficient _____.

5. Ineffective _____.

> *"It could be that one of the greatest hindrances to evangelism today is the poverty of our own experience in evangelism."*
> — Billy Graham

Recommended Resource: Stan Toler's *Practical Guide for Pastoral Ministry*

Vision Planning for Outreach

Where there is no revelation, the people cast off restraint; but blessed is he who keeps the law (Proverbs 29:18).

Stage 1:   Strategic Formation: Where are we now?

Stage 2:   Strategic Development: What does God want us to do?

Stage 3:   Strategic Implementation: How do we get there?

Stage 4:   Strategic Evaluation: How are we doing?

Process Steps	Profound Questions (fog-cutting questions)
D = Direction	What should we do next? Why?
O = Organization	Who is responsible for what? Who is responsible for whom? Do we have the right people in the right places?
C = Cash	What is our projected income, expense, net? Can we afford it? How can we afford it?
T = Tracking	Are we on target?
O = Overall Evaluation	Are we achieving the quality we expect and demand of ourselves?
R = Refinement	How can we be more effective and more efficient (move toward the ideal)?

Source: Bobb Biehl

A New Mentality for Developing Spiritual Communities

All the believers were one in heart and mind. No one claimed that any of his possessions was his own, but they shared everything they had (Acts 4:32).

1. Their spiritual commitment resulted in spiritual _____.

So the churches were strengthened in the faith and grew daily in numbers (Acts 16:5).

2. They employed New Testament _____.

After they prayed, the place where they were meeting was shaken. And they were all filled with the Holy Spirit and spoke the word of God boldly (Acts 4:31).

3. They moved from exclusive to _____.

Then Peter began to speak: "I now realize how true it is that God does not show favoritism but accepts men from every nation who fear him and do what is right" (Acts 10:34-35).

Recommended Resource: *The People Principle* by Stan Toler, and *Each One Win One* by Louie Bustle and Stan Toler.

Realizing the Power of One

"I am going to send you what my Father has promised; but stay in the city until you have been clothed with power from on high" (Luke 24:49).

1. Growth begins with passionate believers.

2. The key to evangelism is not programming, but participation.

> *"It takes the dynamic of God to change an individual and through them we have a great society."*
>
> — Billy Graham

NOTES

WESLEYAN INVESTMENT FOUNDATION
Serving Higher Interests™

Providing
faith based,
loan and savings
opportunities
since 1946.

- Church Loans

- Regular Savings

- IRA Savings

Contact us today for more information:
317.774.7300
info@wifonline.com
www.wifonline.com

A BIBLICAL AND HISTORICAL STRATEGY

"But you will receive power when the Holy Spirit comes on you; and you will be my witnesses in Jerusalem, and in all Judea and Samaria, and to the ends of the earth" (Acts 1:8).

Understanding How the Holy Spirit Worked in the Book of Acts

1. The church _____.

But many who heard the message believed, and the number of men grew to about five thousand (Acts 4:4).

2. The church _____.

So the word of God spread. The number of disciples in Jerusalem increased rapidly, and a large number of priests became obedient to the faith (Acts 6:7)

3. The church _____.

Then the church throughout Judea, Galilee and Samaria enjoyed a time of peace. It was strengthened; and encouraged by the Holy Spirit, it grew in numbers, living in the fear of the Lord (Acts 9:31).

4. The church _____.

The Lord's hand was with them, and a great number of people believed and turned to the Lord (Acts 11:21).

5. The church _____.

But the word of God continued to increase and spread (Acts 12:24).

> "All believers have incredible potential and can impact the world for Christ."
> — Dr. Louie Bustle

Evangelism Doesn't Just Happen

Therefore, I urge you, brothers, in view of God's mercy, to offer your bodies as living sacrifices, holy and pleasing to God—this is your spiritual act of worship. Do not conform any longer to the pattern of this world, but be transformed by the renewing of your mind. Then you will be able to test and approve what God's will is—his good, pleasing and perfect will (Romans 12:1-2).

1. It requires a plan. Acts 13:1

2. It needs biblical principles. Titus 2:1

3. It calls for commitment. Hebrews 10:23

Effective Evangelism Methods

After they prayed, the place where they were meeting was shaken. And they were all filled with the Holy Spirit and spoke the word of God boldly (Acts 4:31).

1. _____ evangelism.

"90 Days of Prayer" Card
My Top Ten Most Wanted List

	Name	Prayed	Invited	Attended	Accepted
1.	_____	_____	_____	_____	_____
2.	_____	_____	_____	_____	_____
3.	_____	_____	_____	_____	_____
4.	_____	_____	_____	_____	_____
5.	_____	_____	_____	_____	_____
6.	_____	_____	_____	_____	_____
7.	_____	_____	_____	_____	_____
8.	_____	_____	_____	_____	_____
9.	_____	_____	_____	_____	_____
10.	_____	_____	_____	_____	_____

2. _____ evangelism.

- Preaching
- Divorce Recovery
- Grief Recovery
- Day Care/Schools
- Community Business Day
- 12-Step Recovery Program
- Counseling
- Small Groups/Sunday School
- English Language Learners
- Financial Freedom

Finding the Unchurched

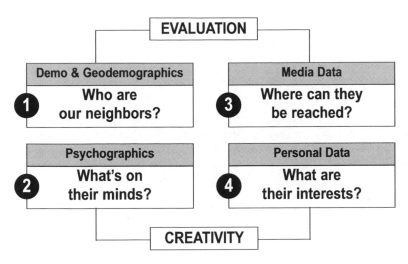

Answer these four questions with the information indicated,
and you'll be more successful in marketing the church.

3. _____ evangelism.

How do people come into a relationship to Christ?

.0001	Percent –	TV or Crusade
1-2	Percent –	Cold Turkey Evangelism
2-4	Percent –	Church Program
3-6	Percent –	Sunday School
6-8	Percent –	"Walk-In"
74	Percent –	Friends or Relatives

The Circle of Friends

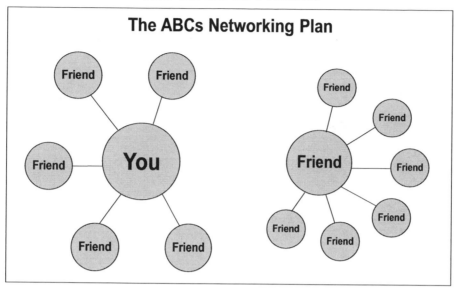

A. Pray for them daily.

B. Share four activities with them during the next year.

Possible Activities

- Sporting Events
- Coffee Shop
- Cook-outs
- Banquets
- Tours
- Fellowship of Christian Athletics
- Community Events

- Shopping
- Civic Clubs
- Golf Outings
- Birthdays/Anniversaries
- Desserts at your place
- Drama at your church
- Breakfasts/Luncheons

C. Invite them to an event for the unchurched.

4. _____ evangelism.

- Concert
- Children's Program
- Christmas Musical
- Holiness Summit
- Friend Day
- Christian Comedy

- Drama
- Easter Musical
- Guest Artist Series
- Seminars
- Pumpkin Patch

Special Note: Design a response form (as illustrated below) for each special event.

Example: At the mid-point of your special event presentation, plan to share the **ABC** plan. Be sure to ask **everyone** to fill out the information form and ask **everyone** to pray

(Sample Special Events Response Form)

CHRISTMAS MUSICAL

Name:_____

Address: _____

City: _____ State: _____ Zip: _____

Phone: _____

TONIGHT, I prayed the **ABC** prayer to invite Jesus Christ to become my personal Savior and Lord.

____ Please send me additional help on the Christian life.

____ I am active in another church.

____ I am a member/regular attender of this church.

____ I would be interested in receiving information on future events.

I heard about Christmas musical from:
- Radio Advertisement
- Newspaper
- Personal Invitation
- Metro Bus
- Other (please specify)

- Television
- Posters
- Friend/Family
- Announcement
- Through this Church

We would sincerely appreciate your comments:

_____

_____

_____

_____

_____

Recommended Resource: *Year-Round Book of Events and Celebrations* by Stan Toler and Elmer Towns

---

5. _____ evangelism.

Projects for Public Places
(Parks, malls, business districts, etc.)

Coffee or soft drink giveaways

Bag packing at self-service groceries

Grocery cart return

Popcorn or popsicle giveaways

Public restroom cleaning

Umbrella escort on rainy days

Free shoe shines

Car drying at self-serve car washes

Doggie cleanup at parks

Laundromat washer/dryer feed

Helium balloon giveaways

Free fishing bait

Christmas gift wrapping

Gatorade giveaway at jogging and biking trails

Projects for Colleges

Pen/pencil giveaways

Free backpacks

Free dorm cleaning

Tutoring

Hot Chocolate giveaway

Bagel giveaway

Projects for Neighborhoods

Leaf raking

Meals for shut-ins

Flower seed packet giveaways

Free bird feeder refills

Window washing

Fireplace kindling giveaways

Sunday morning newspaper and
    coffee giveaway

Projects for Special Occasions:

Mother's Day carnation giveaway

Christmas tree collection and disposal

Easter basket giveaway

Free pizza on moving day

Time change reminder flyers

—Steve Sjogren, *Conspiracy of Kindness*

6. _____ evangelism.

- TV
- Radio
- Yellow Pages

- Newspaper
- Direct Mail
- Website

7. _____ evangelism.

8. _____ evangelism.

> *"Evangelism must not be an optional plan of the local church. It must be an essential priority."*
> — Stan Toler

WESLEYAN INVESTMENT FOUNDATION
Serving Higher Interests™

WIF provides loans for churches and church related organizations in the the Wesleyan Tradition.

Capital projects include:

- New Construction
  - Renovation
  - Relocation
  - Refinance

Competitive Rates

Flexible Terms

Low Closing Costs

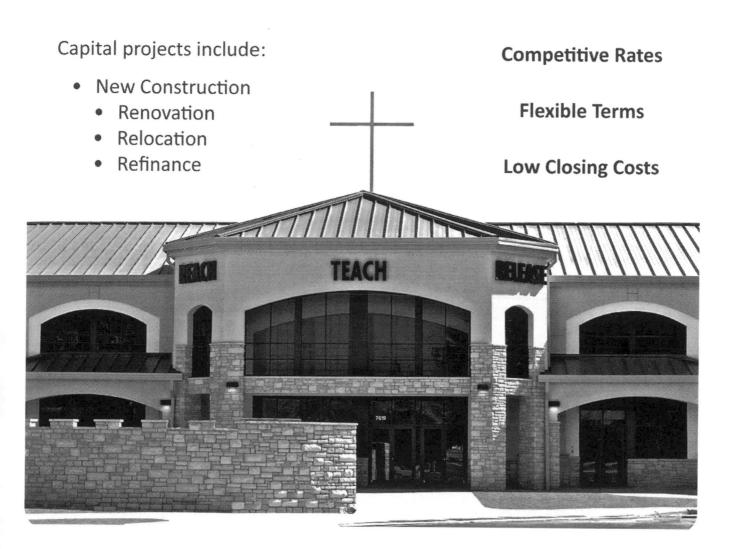

It would be our privilege to be your ministry partner!

Contact us today for more information:
317.774.7300
info@wifonline.com
www.wifonline.com

PREPARING THE CHURCH TO EVANGELIZE

The *ABCs* of Evangelism

"Yet to all who received him, to those who believed in his name, he gave the right to become children of God . . ." (John 1:12).

Mistaken Ways People Think They Can Come to Christ

1. By inheritance.

2. By personal effort.

3. By the desires of others.

Salvation Is Like

1. Receiving a _____. Romans 6:23

2. Coming _____. Luke 15

3. Opening a _____. Revelation 3:20

Recommended Resource: *The ABC's of Evangelism* by Stan Toler

The *ABCs* of a Personal Relationship With Christ

Step One: Pray for the presence of God on your presentation.

Step Two: Always share your testimony.

Step Three: Present the plan to friends and family.

Receiving Jesus Christ is as simple as *ABC* . . .

Admit that you have sinned.   Romans 3:23

Believe that Jesus Christ died for you.   John 1:12

Confess that Jesus Christ is Lord of your life.   Romans 10:9-10

Use the *How to Go to Heaven Pen*, and Begin to share Christ.

Statement: Salvation is a free gift.

Ask: "Would you believe me if I told you that I would give you this pen.

Answer: (usually "yes!")

Response: "But you don't have the pen. What do you need to do to get the pen?"

Answer: (usually) "Reach out and take it!"

Response: "That's right! (Hand the pen to them.) It's yours! **FREE!** And so it is with receiving Christ. You must reach out and take him into your heart by faith." Ephesians 2:8-9.

Step Four: Lead them in a sinner's prayer.

"Dear Lord Jesus, I know that I am a sinner. I believe that You died for my sins and arose from the grave. I now turn from my sins and invite You to come into my heart and life. I receive You as my personal savior and follow You as my Lord. Amen."

Step Five: Give the new Christian assurance of their salvation.

And this is the testimony: God has given us eternal life, and this life is in his Son. He who has the Son has life; he who does not have the Son of God does not have life (1 John 5:11-12).

Recommended Resource: Order How to Go To Heaven Pens www.abcpens.com

NOTES

EACH ONE DISCIPLE ONE

"Therefore go and make disciples of all nations, baptizing them in the name of the Father and of the Son and of the Holy Spirit," (Matthew 28:19).

On Becoming a Disciple

But grow in the grace and knowledge of our Lord and Savior Jesus Christ. To him be glory both now and forever! Amen (2 Peter 3:18).

1. A disciple is a student.

Do your best to present yourself to God as one approved, a workman who does not need to be ashamed and who correctly handles the word of truth (2 Timothy 2:15).

2. A disciple is a steward.

All the believers were together and had everything in common. Selling their possessions and goods, they gave to anyone as he had need (Acts 2:44-45).

3. A disciple is a servant.

Then he said to them all: "If anyone would come after me, he must deny himself and take up his cross daily and follow me" (Luke 9:23).

Recommended Resource: *Growing Disciples*, by Toler, Walters and Casey, and *Each One Disciple One* by Bustle and Toler

WESLEYAN INVESTMENT FOUNDATION
Serving Higher Interests™

Investment opportunities for both individuals and organizations

- Save money

- Earn interest

- Build churches

- Change lives

Save for the things that are important to you and your family and build the Kingdom at the same time!

Contact us today for more information:
317.774.7300
info@wifonline.com
www.wifonline.com

Eight Disciplines of Every Follower of Christ

1. Pursuing holiness.

Therefore, I urge you, brothers, in view of God's mercy, to offer your bodies as living sacrifices, holy and pleasing to God—this is your spiritual act of worship. Do not conform any longer to the pattern of this world, but be transformed by the renewing of your mind. Then you will be able to test and approve what God's will is—his good, pleasing and perfect will (Romans 12:1-2).

2. Private worship.

Let us then approach the throne of grace with confidence, so that we may receive mercy and find grace to help us in our time of need (Hebrews 4:16).

3. Public worship.

Worship the Lord with gladness; come before him with joyful songs (Psalm 100:2).

4. Observing sacraments.

Therefore, whoever eats the bread or drinks the cup of the Lord in an unworthy manner will be guilty of sinning against the body and blood of the Lord. A man ought to examine himself before he eats of the bread and drinks of the cup. For anyone who eats and drinks without recognizing the body of the Lord eats and drinks judgment on himself (1 Corinthians 11:27-29).

5. Personal witnessing.

He told them, "This is what is written: The Christ will suffer and rise from the dead on the third day, and repentance and forgiveness of sins will be preached in his name to all nations, beginning at Jerusalem. You are witnesses of these things. I am going to send you what my Father has promised; but stay in the city until you have been clothed with power from on high" (Luke 24:46-48).

6. Personal discipline.

"But I have prayed for you, Simon, that your faith may not fail. And when you have turned back, strengthen your brothers" (Luke 22:32).

7. Biblical stewardship.

The earth is the Lord's, and everything in it, the world, and all who live in it; (Psalm 24:1)

8. Church membership.

Husbands, love your wives, just as Christ loved the church and gave himself up for her to make her holy, cleansing her by the washing with water through the word, and to present her to himself as a radiant church, without stain or wrinkle or any other blemish, but holy and blameless (Ephesians 5:25-27).

Pastor's Welcome Class	Gifts Discovery Class	Discipleship Class
Week 1 – Vision	Week 1 – Personality Profiles	Week 1 – Beliefs
Week 2 – Confidence	Week 2 – Interest and Skills	Week 2 – Core Values
Week 3 – Communication	Week 3 – Spiritual Gifts 1	Week 3 – Stewardship
Week 4 – Family	Week 4 – Spiritual Gifts 2	Week 4 – Lay Ministry
4 Weeks	4 Weeks	4 Weeks

Recommended Resource: *The Secret Blend,* and *The Richest Person in the World* by Stan Toler

NOTES

OVERVIEW

Introduction: Fulfilling the Great Commission has never been more important—and has never been more possible. God has blessed the church with the power of His Spirit and Spirit-directed tools and methods for introducing others to Christ.

Power of One is a practical resource for motivating and training believers—one by one—to expedite the work of Kingdom-building. A vibrant church is one which uses every available means to reach every available person or people group.

Mission: The mission of *Power of One* is to obey Christ's command to evangelize unbelievers, disciple believers, and multiply churches.

Vision: The vision of *Power of One* is to motivate believers to use their spiritual gifts in praying, witnessing, teaching, and organizing events that will introduce unbelievers to Christ.

Theme: The theme of *Power of One* is a biblical response to the proclamation of the Great Commandment (Matthew 28:18-20) and the "Great Provision" (Acts 1:8).

Materials: *Power of One* utilizes several simple and yet effective resource components:
    Letters to inform and inspire believers to the task of Kingdom-building.
    Bulletin inserts (Spanish included) to help create community around evangelism and discipleship objectives—and the theme of the campaign.
    Wristbands to create next-generation awareness of the opportunity to influence others with life-changing truths.
    Lessons (Spanish included) for classes or small groups of all ages, teaching the principles of prayer, witnessing, discipleship, and outreach.

Sermon outlines, sermons, and PowerPoint for adults, youth and children (Spanish included) to help pastors and staff preach and teach God's plan of salvation, sanctification and discipleship.

Additional resources:

ABC's of Evangelism Notebook (www.StanToler.com)

Each One Win One book (www.StanToler.com)

Each One Disciple One book (www.StanToler.com)

Growing Disciples book (www.StanToler.com)

 **VISION STATEMENT**

Participating passionately in worship.   **Worship**

Opening doors for authentic friendship.   **Friendship**

Working with the community in partnership.   **Partnership**

Employing our resources in stewardship.   **Stewardship**

Reflecting Christ through our discipleship.   **Discipleship**

"But you will be my witnesses in Jerusalem, and in all Judea and Samaria, and to the ends of the earth" (Acts 1:8)

LAUNCHING *THE POWER OF ONE*

As Jesus was walking beside the Sea of Galilee, he saw two brothers, Simon called Peter and his brother Andrew. They were casting a net into the lake, for they were fishermen. "Come, follow me," Jesus said, "and I will make you fishers of men." At once they left their nets and followed him (Matthew 4:18-20).

1. Communicate the dream.

2. Organize the plan.

    -   Preaching Plan
    -   Bulletin Inserts
    -   ABC Pens
    -   Small Group Lessons

    -   Wristbands
    -   Most Wanted Cards
    -   Letters written
    -   Order Support Resources

3. Plan the calendar.

    -   40 Day Vision Emphasis
    -   Invitation Sundays (4)
    -   Outreach Events (4)
    -   Celebrations (12) Baptisms, Dedications, etc.
    -   Discipleship Class Launch
    -   Holiness Summit
    -   Order Resource Materials
    -   Ministry Recognition
    -   Celebration of the Harvest

THE POWER OF ONE SERMON OUTLINES

Sermon Outline One

"The Power of One"

Ephesians 4:16

From him the whole body, joined and held together by every supporting ligament, grows and builds itself up in love, as each part does its work.

You've heard it said, "There's *one* in every crowd." Guess what? You're the *ONE*!

The Power of One Standard Ephesians 4:1-3

1. **The example of biblical leaders.**
2. **The miraculous birth of Jesus Christ.**

> *"We have the example of the prophets and of our Lord Jesus Christ. We must unite to win our world, now."*
> – Talmadge Johnson

The Power of One Spiritual Process vv. 4-7

1. **One body.**
2. **One spirit.**
3. **One hope.**

> *"We really do need each other."*
> – Reuben Welch

The Power of ONENESS in Christ vv. 8-16

1. **We anticipate the future with joy.**   Revelation 21:1-7
2. **We reach out to win the lost.**   Matthew 28:18-20

> *"Every believer has at least one spiritual gift and should use it for God's glory."*
> – Louie Bustle

Sermon Outline Two

"The Power of Prayer"

Psalm 143:1

O LORD, hear my prayer, listen to my cry for mercy; in your faithfulness and righteousness come to my relief.

The writings of Israel's greatest king, David, are a powerful combination of songs and prayers. Psalm 143 is a prayer for deliverance from the enemy.

David Believed God's Kingdom Would Never Be Defeated vv. 2-4

Do not bring your servant into judgment, for no one living is righteous before you. The enemy pursues me, he crushes me to the ground; he makes me dwell in darkness like those long dead. So my spirit grows faint within me; my heart within me is dismayed.

1. **He trusted God when he didn't know the way.**
2. **He relied on God when he faced the enemy.**
3. **He rested in God when He needed forgiveness.**

David Believed God's Resources Would Never Be Exhausted v. 5

I remember the days of long ago; I meditate on all your works and consider what your hands have done. I remember the days of long ago; I meditate on all your works and consider what your hands have done.

1. **He remembered God's refreshing.** v. 6
    I spread out my hands to you; my soul thirsts for you like a parched land.

2. **He remembered God's presence.** v. 8
    Let the morning bring me word of your unfailing love, for I have put my trust in you. Show me the way I should go, for to you I lift up my soul.

3. **He remembered God's deliverance.** v. 9
    Rescue me from my enemies, O LORD, for I hide myself in you.

> *"Reflecting on the faithfulness of God gives us strength for trusting in the promises of God."*
> – Stan Toler

David Believed God's Calling Would Never Be Rescinded v. 10

Teach me to do your will, for you are my God; may your good Spirit lead me on level ground.

1. **He prayed for direction.** v. 10
2. **He prayed for protection.** v. 11

   For your name's sake, O Lord, preserve my life; in your righteousness, bring me out of trouble.

> *"Prayer is depending on God for the outcome."*
> – E. M. Bounds

Sermon Outline Three

"The Power of Friendship"
John 15:13-15

"Greater love has no one than this, that he lay down his life for his friends. You are my friends if you do what I command. I no longer call you servants, because a servant does not know his master's business. Instead, I have called you friends, for everything that I learned from my Father I have made known to you."

Jesus could have expressed His relationship with His disciples in many ways: coworker, master, teacher, leader, creator; but He was the fulfillment of the Bible's prophetic word, a "friend who sticks closer than a brother."

Intentional Friendship Shows Spiritual Authenticity v. 13b

". . .lay down his life for his friends."

1. **Friends are willing to go to any length for the welfare of another.**
2. **Intentional friendship is willing to make personal sacrifices.**

Intentional Friendship Shows Mutual Responsibility v. 14

"You are my friends if you do what I command."

1. **Friendship isn't a one-way street.**
2. **Intentional friendship builds on common trust and interests.**

Intentional Friendship Shows Personal Reliability v. 15b

". . .I have called you friends,"

1. **Friendship is a way of saying, "You can depend on me."**
2. **Intentional friendship is visible, and is a way of saying "I am depending on Christ, so you can depend on me."**

Intentional Friendship Shows Potential Accountability v. 15c

". . . everything that I learned . . . I have made known to you."

1. **Friendship is a continuing investment of time, energy and resources.**
2. **Intentional friendship is a spiritual investment for the good of another.**

"Evangelism is not an optional plan for the church. It is an essential priority."
–Stan Toler

Sermon Outline Four

"The Power of Invitation"
Matthew 4:18-20

As Jesus was walking beside the Sea of Galilee, he saw two brothers, Simon called Peter and his brother Andrew. They were casting a net into the lake, for they were fishermen. "Come, follow me," Jesus said, "and I will make you fishers of men." At once they left their nets and followed him.

Each of us has received an invitation with the letters, RSVP engraved on a reply card. According to the Merriam-Webster dictionary, RSVP is an abbreviation for a French word which translated simply means: Respond if you please.

A Personal Invitation with a Powerful Directive: *"Follow Me."* v. 19a
1. It wasn't an invitation to follow a set of principles.
2. It wasn't an invitation to follow an organization.
3. It was an invitation to follow a person.
   Who am I?
   Why am I here?
   Where am I going?

A Personal Invitation with a Powerful Dynamic: *"I Will Make You."* v. 19b
1. A dynamic that makes something out of nothing.
2. A dynamic that destroys sin and empowers our potential.

A Personal Invitation with a Powerful Dimension: *"Fishers of Men."* v. 19b
1. Turned the common into the uncommon.
2. Turned the mundane into the miraculous.

> *"For God so loved the world that he gave his one and only Son, that whoever believes in him shall not perish but have eternal life" (John 3:16).*

The Power of One

A study in one major city indicated that out of eleven million drivers on its streets, only fifty percent could read a road map. Researchers concluded that in most cases, map reading was being replaced by a reliance on navigational systems. But as you may know, even the best GPS can lead to a dead end.

Someone you know is looking for spiritual directions. They need to know the right way, but they are relying on the wrong sources. God has already given them a road map: The Bible.

Someone needs a trusted friend—like you—to show them how to read the map. Someone who will prayerfully guide them. **There is power in one.**

"But you will receive power when the Holy Spirit comes upon you. And you will be my witnesses, telling people about me everywhere" (Acts 1:8 NLT).

The Power of One

A study in one major city indicated that out of eleven million drivers on its streets, only fifty percent could read a road map. Researchers concluded that in most cases, map reading was being replaced by a reliance on navigational systems. But as you may know, even the best GPS can lead to a dead end.

Someone you know is looking for spiritual directions. They need to know the right way, but they are relying on the wrong sources. God has already given them a road map: The Bible.

Someone needs a trusted friend—like you—to show them how to read the map. Someone who will prayerfully guide them. **There is power in one.**

"But you will receive power when the Holy Spirit comes upon you. And you will be my witnesses, telling people about me everywhere" (Acts 1:8 NLT).

The Power of Prayer

It's always there, but you can't see it. The airwaves are filled with billions of thoughts—words of wisdom, instructions, affirmations, and directions—bouncing off satellites orbiting thousands of miles above the earth to a receiver you can hold in your hand. The Creator is the mind behind it—and you are His receiver. What He says to you in prayer, and what you say to Him, will not only change your life, it will change the life of another. **There is power in one.**

"But you will receive power when the Holy Spirit comes upon you. And you will be my witnesses, telling people about me everywhere" (Acts 1:8 NLT).

The Power of Prayer

It's always there, but you can't see it. The airwaves are filled with billions of thoughts—words of wisdom, instructions, affirmations, and directions—bouncing off satellites orbiting thousands of miles above the earth to a receiver you can hold in your hand. The Creator is the mind behind it—and you are His receiver. What He says to you in prayer, and what you say to Him, will not only change your life, it will change the life of another. **There is power in one.**

"But you will receive power when the Holy Spirit comes upon you. And you will be my witnesses, telling people about me everywhere" (Acts 1:8 NLT).

The Power of Friendship

Think of that one person who made the greatest spiritual impact on your life. What did they say? What did they do? What was it about their life? Most likely they were just living like Jesus. After dying on the Cross and rising from the grave, Jesus sent His Holy Spirit to live in and through His followers. You can be that one person who will make the greatest spiritual impact on the life of another. **There is power in one.**

"But you will receive power when the Holy Spirit comes upon you. And you will be my witnesses, telling people about me everywhere"(Acts 1:8 NLT).

The Power of Friendship

Think of that one person who made the greatest spiritual impact on your life. What did they say? What did they do? What was it about their life? Most likely they were just living like Jesus. After dying on the Cross and rising from the grave, Jesus sent His Holy Spirit to live in and through His followers. You can be that one person who will make the greatest spiritual impact on the life of another. **There is power in one.**

"But you will receive power when the Holy Spirit comes upon you. And you will be my witnesses, telling people about me everywhere"(Acts 1:8 NLT).

The Power of Invitation

You open the envelope and read: *You are cordially invited . . .* You WERE on the list! You wondered if you would receive the invitation. There were moments when you thought you had been left out. But you weren't. You hadn't received your invitation. Now it is in your hand. Now you can be a part of the celebration; and it's all because someone took the time to give you an invitation.

Being a witness for Jesus is simply giving an invitation to someone who thought they had been left out. **There is power in one.**

"But you will receive power when the Holy Spirit comes upon you. And you will be my witnesses, telling people about me everywhere" (Acts 1:8 NLT).

The Power of Invitation

You open the envelope and read: *You are cordially invited . . .* You WERE on the list! You wondered if you would receive the invitation. There were moments when you thought you had been left out. But you weren't. You hadn't received your invitation. Now it is in your hand. Now you can be a part of the celebration; and it's all because someone took the time to give you an invitation.

Being a witness for Jesus is simply giving an invitation to someone who thought they had been left out. **There is power in one.**

"But you will receive power when the Holy Spirit comes upon you. And you will be my witnesses, telling people about me everywhere" (Acts 1:8 NLT).

The Power of One Letters   **Letter One: The Power of One**

(Date)

Dear (Name),

Isn't it amazing how God trusts so much to so few.

One person, Adam, was given the task of naming all the animals that God had just created. God chose one person, Moses, to meet with Him on Mt. Sinai and gave him the Ten Commandments—God's eternal law.

Jesus, God's only Son, continued the family tradition. One by one He chose followers to become His disciples—entrusting them with the greatest mission of all time: sharing the good news of the gospel with a society that was stuck in the mud of bad news.

You and I are about to launch one of the most exciting ventures in the history of our church! It is a life-transforming project called *The Power of One*.

Together, we are going to see miracles. Broken hearts will be healed. Shattered relationships will be put back together. People without hope will receive hope. And you and I will be forever changed!

I'll tell you all about it this weekend. And I'll tell you how you can be an army of one who can make an eternal difference in the life of another person.

One plus God's power is a major force for holiness.

Until we meet in the Lord's house,

Pastor (Name)
P. S. Read Ephesians 4 this week. You'll see what I'm talking about!

The Power of One Letters   **Letter Two: The Power of Invitation**

(Date)

Dear (Name),

What if you had to understand everything there is to know about electronics to place a cell phone call or send a text message?

Relax; you don't have to. All you have to do is make the call or send the text. Your cell phone provider will do all the work.

I know what you're thinking, and you're right! That sounds a lot like prayer. You make the call and your Provider takes over.

Did you hear about those one-hundred-and-twenty people who met on the second floor of a Jerusalem building in Bible times? They called on God in prayer—and it brought the house down! Well, almost. The Bible says the place where they met was "shaken."

I'll tell you all about it this weekend. It's all part of life-transforming project called *The Power of One*. You and I will discover how the power of prayer can do some shaking in our world. Walls of bitterness and resentment will crumble. Prisons of guilt and despair will open up.

I can hardly wait for the weekend services! God wants us to share the joy that Christ gives, so He INCLUDED THE BATTERIES.

Come, discover the power.

Pastor (Name)

P. S. Stop by the sanctuary of the Psalms this week. Check out room #143. You'll see that the Psalmist David really has an edge on getting in touch with God!

The Power of One Letters   **Letter Three: The Power of Friendship**

(Date)

Dear (Name),

The word has only six letters and has a consonant on each end. The middle letter of the word makes it complete. It's the letter "i." There may not be an "I" in church, but there is an important "I" in this word: F-R-I-E-N-D.

Confused yet? Wait, there's more. Without "U," there wouldn't be an "I" in friend. I know that sounds a little trite, but it's true. You are the one—a power of one—that makes the difference in being an F-R-I-E-N-D or just being an acquaintance.

I'm sure you know there are levels of friendship. You have friends—and then you have a "best friend." Best friends are second-level friends. They're reliable, accountable, trusting, and helpful.

We've been talking about *The Power of One* the last two weeks: The power of one person realizing the importance of using their abilities for God's kingdom and the power of one person's prayer for another person. This weekend, I will be teaching on the power of friendship—the unbelievable power of connection.

You and I have started this incredible journey together—discovering how God's life-transforming power can be a force for holiness. Bring your Bible and an open heart. We're just getting started!

Your F-R-I-E-N-D,

Pastor (Name)

P.S. The apostle John was called the apostle of love. Read John 15 this week, and discover what he has to say about the power of friendship.

The Power of One Letters   **Letter Four: The Power of Invitation**

(Date)

Dear (Name),

According to one online dictionary, "RSVP" is from a French word which means "Respond if you please." You'll probably find an RSVP enclosed in an invitation to a celebration or event.

What if God Himself were to send you an invitation—written on heaven's stationery, and delivered by HPS (Heaven's Parcel Service)? And what if it arrived at the very moment you needed it most in your life? Here's the good news, He has! The most powerful invitation ever given was hand-delivered by Jesus Christ. The "receipt," marked "paid in full," is written in the pages of God's Word.

Someone you know needs an invitation like that. You can be a *Power of One* in someone's life—just when they need it most. I'll tell you all about it this weekend.

You won't need to "respond if you please." Just come with an open heart and discover how you can be a force for holiness.

Cordially yours,

Pastor (Name)

P. S. Whether online or in print, search for Matthew 4 in the Bible. See what God's Word says about the power of an invitation.

WORKBOOK SPONSORS

WESLEYAN INVESTMENT FOUNDATION
Serving Higher Interests™

Free financial seminars now available!

The goal of these seminars is to highlight the importance of supporting the ministries of the local church as well as the Kingdom and stewardship benefits of investing with WIF.

- Presented during a time that works the best for your church family.

- No cost to the local church.

- WIF provides the refreshments!

Contact us today for more information:
317.774.7300
info@wifonline.com
www.wifonline.com

BUILD A KIT
BUILD YOUR TEAM
MAKE AN IMPACT.

You can make a difference in the lives of people around the world by hosting a kit assembly event.

Your team will build specialized kits that directly impact the health and well-being of children, women and men in need.

PowrServ events benefit
Heart to Heart International.

HEART to HEART
INTERNATIONAL
hearttoheart.org

Contact:

Bethany Williams
913.538.7892
bethany.williams@powrserv.org

@PowrServ
Facebook.com/PowrServ

POWRSERV™

Christian Healthcare Ministries
The biblical solution to healthcare costs
www.chministries.org

ACCREDITED CHARITY
bbb.org
BBB

passion
devotion
collaboration
VISION health
love good freedom
ministry Galatians 6:2
devotion family INTEGRITY
transparency prayerfulness
LEADERSHIP passion wisdom
freedom confidence
Galatians 6:2 collaboration
prayerfulness
biblical

Galatians 6:2
passion
love
freedom health
family
VISION health
confidence ministry
good LEADERSHIP
passion family
INTEGRITY
wisdom VISION devotion
transparency
wisdom
love collaboration

1.800.791.6225
www.facebook.com/christianhealthcareministries
www.chministries.org

35 YEARS

One sponsor can transform One child's life forever.

The Power of One: YOU!

For $27 a month, YOU can give a Hand Up to a child in need through Shepherd Community Center. Shepherd works with neighborhood youth and their families to break the cycle of poverty on the near eastside of Indianapolis. A core set of programs make up our Continuum of Care, which is available to participants from birth through adulthood.

By becoming a sponsor, you will be providing a Hand Up to a child in need in Indianapolis.

COULD THIS BE **YOUR** OPPORTUNITY TO HELP?

HandUpForIndy.org

4107 E Washington Street
Indianapolis, IN 46201

p. 317.375.0203

shepherdcommunity.org

breaking the cycle of poverty

shepherd community center

Hand Up
Give a hand up to a child in need through
Shepherd Community Center

☐ I commit to a gift of $27 per month.

Name _____

Address _____

City _____ State _____ Zip _____

Phone _____ Email _____

Church Affiliation _____

Payment Information

☐ Check # _____ Amount _____

☐ Credit Card — ☐ Visa ☐ MasterCard ☐ AMEX ☐ Discover
(Please charge my credit card each month)

Name on Card: _____

Card #: _____ CVV _____ Expires ____ / ____

Signature _____

☐ Electronic Funds Transfer   Account Type ☐ Checking ☐ Savings
(please include a voided check)

Account No. _____ Routing No. _____

☐ I would like to receive my receipts via email

STewardship PAYROLL SERVICES

Working with ministries nationwide!

As little as $2 per person, per payroll period

✓ **Easy to use**
✓ **Totally on-line**
✓ **Secure**
✓ **No year-end or W-2 fees**

CONTACT: Gerry Washington
866-604-8880, ext.706

gerry@stewardshiptechnology.com
www.stewardshippayroll.com

AMERICA'S CHRISTIAN
C R E D I T   U N I O N

proud partner of

stewardship
technology
serving the church through technology

ELECTRONIC GIVING SOLUTIONS

The secure and economical way to accept donations electronically!

Designed specifically for your church or ministries unique needs. Electronic Giving Solutions by Stewardship Technology provides a safe and secure way to accept tithes, offerings and general donations.

With Electronic Giving Solutions, you can:
- Turn occasional givers into consistent year-round donors
- Improve your ability to predict cash flow
- Access donor data through our online Beneficiary Web
- Easily download accounting reports
- Provide donors with a simple, fast way to manage their giving

IS YOUR CHURCH ONLINE?

GET STARTED TODAY!
Call **Gerry at 866-604-8880, ext. 706** or go to **www.egsnetwork.com**

Stewardship Technology, Inc. Mount Vernon, OH 43050 | www.StewardshipTechnology.com

stewardship
technology
serving the church through technology

TOLER LEADERSHIP

Call 405.603.7110 | Fax 405.603.7120 | Email info@tolerleadership.com

Mail: PO Box 720230 – Oklahoma City OK 73172

Humor/Inspiration	QTY	RETAIL PRICE	SALE PRICE	TOTAL PRICE
Buzzards Are Circling But God's Not Finished With Me Yet		$15.00	$10.00	
God Has Never Failed Me, But He's Sure Scared Me To Death A Few Times		$15.00	$10.00	
God Can Do Anything But Fail, So Try Parasailing In A Windstorm - NEW		$15.00	$10.00	
ReThink Your Life		$22.00	$10.00	
ReThink Your Life Journal		$10.00	$5.00	
That Ain't Just Preaching		$13.00	$5.00	
You Might Be a Preacher If (BEST OF)		$7.00	$5.00	
You've Been Around the Church a Long Time		$7.00	$5.00	
Minute Motivator Series				
Minute Motivators for Dieters		$7.00	$5.00	
Minute Motivators for Graduates		$7.00	$5.00	
Minute Motivators For Leaders		$7.00	$5.00	
Minute Motivators for Men		$7.00	$5.00	
Minute Motivators for the Military - NEW		$7.00	$5.00	
Minute Motivators for New Believers - NEW		$7.00	$5.00	
Minute Motivators for Teachers		$7.00	$5.00	
Minute Motivators for Teens		$7.00	$5.00	
Minute Motivators for Women		$7.00	$5.00	
Minute Motivators for Athletes		$7.00	$5.00	
Leadership				
The Exceptional Leader		$16.00	$10.00	
The Relational Leader		$18.00	$10.00	
The Secret Blend		$18.00	$10.00	
Outstanding! Leadership that Motivates and Relates - NEW		$14.00	$10.00	
Terrific! Five Star Customer Service - NEW		$11.00	$10.00	
Total Quality Life		$15.00	$10.00	
How to Capture Your Thought Life		$8.00	$5.00	
How to Shape Up Your Health		$8.00	$5.00	
How to Gain Control of Your Finances		$8.00	$5.00	
How to Strengthen Your Faith		$8.00	$5.00	
Pastoral Resources				
The Case of Stuart's Ship (Children's Book)		$15.00	$10.00	
Each One Win One		$30.00	$10.00	
Each One Disciple One		$30.00	$10.00	
Give to Live		$17.00	$10.00	
ReThink Your Life		$20.00	$10.00	
Stan Toler's Practical Guide for Pastoral Ministry		$18.00	$10.00	
Stan Toler's Practical Guide for Hiring Staff		$15.00	$5.00	
Stan Toler's Practical Guide for Ministry Transition		$15.00	$5.00	
Stan Toler's Practical Guide for Leading Church Boards		$15.00	$5.00	
Stan Toler's Practical Guide for Leading Staff		$15.00	$5.00	
Stan Toler's Practical Guide for Solo Ministry		$15.00	$5.00	
Devotions for Ministry Couples		$15.00	$5.00	
Devotions for Pastors		$15.00	$5.00	
The Five Star Church		$17.00	$10.00	
The Vibrant Church		$13.00	$5.00	
You Might Be a Preacher If (BEST OF)		$7.00	$5.00	
You've Been Around the Church a Long Time		$7.00	$5.00	
He Still Speaks – Toler Brothers CD		$20.00	$5.00	
			TOTAL	

Ordering Options

PO Box 720230 – Oklahoma City, OK 73172 | Phone 405-603-7110 (CREDIT CARD)| Fax 405-603-7120

Books for Annual Special Events

JANUARY – Stewardship Emphasis
- ☐ *Give to Live - $17.99*
- ☐ *How to Gain Control of Your Finances - $7.99*
- ☐ *ReThink Your Life - 22.99*
- ☐ *ReThink Journal - $9.99*
- ☐ *Minute Motivators for Dieters - $6.99*

FEBRUARY – Valentines Day Emphasis
- ☐ *Devotions for Ministry Couples - $12.99*

MARCH – Outreach and Evangelism Emphasis
- ☐ *The Secret Blend - $17.99*
- ☐ *Minute Motivators for New Believers - $6.99*
- ☐ *Each One Win One - $29.99*
- ☐ *Each One Disciple One - $29.99*

APRIL – Memorial Day Emphasis
- ☐ *Minute Motivators for the Military - $6.99*

MAY – Mother's Day Emphasis
- ☐ *Minute Motivators for Women - $6.99*
- ☐ *Buzzards Are Circling; But God's Not Finished With Me Yet - $14.99*
- ☐ *God's Never Failed Me; But He's Sure Scared Me To Death A Few Times - $14.99*

JUNE – Dad and Grad's Day Emphasis
- ☐ *Minute Motivators for Graduates - $6.99*
- ☐ *The Winning Dad - $12.99*
- ☐ *Minute Motivators for Men - $6.99*
- ☐ *Minute Motivators for Athletes - $6.99*

JULY – Leadership/Church Boards
- ☐ *The Exceptional Leader - $15.99*

- ☐ *Minute Motivators for Leaders - $6.99*
- ☐ *Practical Guide for Church Boards - $14.99*
- ☐ *Practical Guide for Hiring Staff - $14.99*
- ☐ *Practical Guide for Hiring Staff - $14.99*
- ☐ *Practical Guide for Solo Ministry - $14.99*
- ☐ *Practical Guide for Ministry Transition - $14.99*

AUGUST – Youth/Teacher Emphasis
- ☐ *Minute Motivators for Teens - $6.99*
- ☐ *Minute Motivators for Teachers - $6.99*

SEPTEMBER – Outreach and Evangelism
- ☐ *The Relational Leader - $17.99*
- ☐ *Minute Motivators for New Believers - $6.99*
- ☐ *Total Quality Life - $14.99*

OCTOBER – Pastor Appreciation
- ☐ *Devotions for Pastors*
- ☐ *The Best of You Might Be A Preacher if... - $6.99*
- ☐ *That Ain't Just Preaching; A View From the Back Pew - $13.00*
- ☐ *You've Know You've Been Around Church Too Long.... - $6.99*
- ☐ *Pastor's Practical Guide For Ministry - $17.99*

NOVEMBER – Veteran's Day
- ☐ *Minute Motivators for the Military - $6.99*

DECEMBER – Year End Giving/Donor Gifts
- ☐ *How to Strengthen Your Faith - $7.99*
- ☐ *How to Shape Up Your Health - $7.99*
- ☐ *How to Capture Your Thought Life - $7.99*
- ☐ *How To Gain Control of Your Finances - $7.99*

Pricing Breakdown

Books that **retail for $10.00 or more are $5.00 each** in quantities of 25 or more. (Plus Shipping)

Books that **retail for less than $10.00 are $3.00 each** in quantities of 25 or more. (Plus Shipping)

For descriptions and images of each book please visit **www.StanToler.com**

Ordering Options

PO Box 720230 – Oklahoma City, OK 73172 | Phone 405-603-7110 | Fax 405-603-7120

Info@ABCPens.com

405-603-7110

Customer Name_____

Ship To Address_____

City_____)_____ **State**_____ **Zip**_____

Telephone_____ **Email**_____

1-25 Pens	$2.00 Each
25 Pens or More	$1.00 Each

Billing Information: (Credit Card, Check, or Money Order)

Number of Pens _____ x $2.00 (or $1.00 for 25 or more) = $_____

Name on Credit Card_____

Type of Credit Card _____Visa _____MasterCard

Credit Card Number_____ Exp. Date_____

Signature_____ 3# Security Code: _____ (On back of Card)

Mail Your Order and Check to:

ABC Pens PO Box 721243 - Oklahoma City, OK 73172

FREE UPS GROUND SHIPPING!

The Power of One

This is to certify that

has completed The Power of One training conference involving four hours of instruction, to be transferred into the amount of continuing education credits as determined by the certificate holder's crediting organization.

Awarded _____ **(Date), in** _____ **(City/State)**

Stan Toler, Instructor

" ...when the wise are instructed, they receive knowledge"
Proverbs 21:11.

31109924R00032

Made in the USA
San Bernardino, CA
03 March 2016